Tiny and the big wave

By Annette Smith
Illustrated by Julian Bruere

2

Mum and Dad and Matt
went for a walk with Tiny.

Tiny ran all the way
down to the beach.

4

"Tiny!" shouted Matt.
"Come back!
  Here is your lead."

Tiny ran after the seagulls.
"Woof!" she said. "Woof!"

Away went the seagulls.

6

Tiny ran up and down.

She ran into the water after the seagulls.

"Tiny!" shouted Dad.
"Come back here!"

A big wave
came up
the beach.

"Oh, **no!**"
cried Matt.
"Where is Tiny?"

9

Dad ran into the waves
to look for Tiny.

"Stay here with me, Matt,"
said Mum.

Matt looked at the big waves
and he cried.

"I can see Tiny!" shouted Dad.
He went out to get her.

"Here she is,
   Matt," he said.
"Tiny is safe."

"I'm all wet," said Dad.
"I'm going home."

"And I'm wet, too," said Matt.

"Come on," said Mum.
"Here is Tiny's lead."

Tiny walked home
with her lead **on**.

"Good dog, Tiny,"
said Matt.